BOYZ RULE!

Battle of the Games

Felice Arena and Phil Kettle

illustrated by
Gus Gordon

First published 2003 by
MACMILLAN EDUCATION AUSTRALIA PTY LTD
627 Chapel Street, South Yarra, Australia 3141

This edition first published in the United States of America
in 2004 by MONDO Publishing.

For information contact:
MONDO Publishing
980 Avenue of the Americas
New York, NY 10018

Visit our web site at http://www.mondopub.com

04 05 06 07 08 09   9 8 7 6 5 4 3 2 1

ISBN 1-59336-372-9 (PB)

Library of Congress Cataloging-in-Publication Data

Arena, Felice, 1968-
   Battle of the games / Felice Arena and Phil Kettle ; illustrated by Gus Gordon.
   p. cm. -- (Boyz rule!)
   Summary: Luis and Billy spend a rainy day inside playing games. Includes
   related facts about games as well as questions to test the reader's
   comprehension.
   ISBN: 1-59336-372-9 (pbk.)
   [1. Games--Fiction. 2. Competition (Psychology)--Fiction.] I. Kettle, Phil, 1955-
   II. Gordon, Gus, ill. III. Title.

PZ7.A6825Bat 2004
[E]--dc22
                                                              2004040270

Project Management by Limelight Press Pty Ltd
Cover and text design by Lore Foye
Illustrations by Gus Gordon

Printed in Hong Kong

Contents

Luis   Billy

CHAPTER 1

Rain Games

Best friends Billy and Luis are
hanging out together one rainy
Saturday at Billy's house.

Billy "I wish the rain would stop.
Then we could ride our bikes."

Luis "Yeah. It's really coming down. You sure your mom won't let us play outside?"

Billy "Nah. I've already asked a million times. She said we should be able to entertain ourselves *indoors*."

Luis "So, what are we gonna do?"

Billy "Wanna watch TV? Or a DVD?"

Luis "Nah. I've seen all the movies you've got."

Billy "No you haven't. What about *Killer Bunnies*?"

Luis "Seen it!"

Billy "You sure? The one where a bunch of rabbits grow really long fangs and take over a small town?"

Luis "And they're as tall as the humans—yeah, I've seen it."

Billy "Okay then, wanna play a game? I have a new computer game called 'Super Hero Racing.'"

Luis "Cool!"

Billy and Luis sit in front of Billy's computer. Billy explains the rules of the game to Luis while it's loading.

Billy "You've got ten superheroes to pick from. Once you choose the hero you're gonna be, you have to race each other around the world. You have to jump over mountains and bust through buildings. You can fly, run, or swim. The first one back to the starting place is the winner. I'm gonna be Super Bull Man...half-man, half-bull."

Luis "I'll be Super Stallican...
half-stallion, half-pelican."
Billy "Okay. Ready, go!"

Billy and Luis frantically click and
move their joysticks. It's a close race
but Billy makes it over the finish
line first.

Billy "Yes! In your face! I'm the winner! Champion of the world! And you're the loser! Woo-hoo!"

Billy begins to do a funny dance in front of Luis.

Luis "What are you doing?"

Billy "It's my victory dance. Yeah!
I'm the greatest! And you're not!"

Luis "It's only one game. And now
that I know what to do, I challenge
you to a rematch. And this time
I'll beat ya!"

Billy "Okay, you're on!"

CHAPTER 2

Show Me the Money

Billy and Luis play another game of "Super Hero Racing." Again, Billy is the winner and again he rubs it in Luis's face. Luis wants to keep playing until he wins. Twenty games later he still hasn't beaten his friend.

Luis "I hate this game."

Billy "You're just saying that
because you can't beat me. Ha, ha!"

Luis "Well, let's play something else.
Then you'll see who's laughing."

Billy "Okay! But I gotta tell you
I'm the king of all games!
Computer games, board games,
whatever. You won't be able to
beat me at any of them."

Luis "Yeah, right. Just you wait and see…king of big heads!"

Billy "Okay, forget the computer. How about Monopoly®?"

Luis "Now you're talking, dude!"

Billy and Luis set up the Monopoly® board on the kitchen table. Billy decides to be "banker" and deals out some money to himself and Luis. The boys choose their markers.

Billy "I get the dog!"

Luis "I'll be the car!"

Billy "First, we have to toss the die. Whoever gets the highest number starts. Here goes...6! Yes!"

Luis rolls the dice. It shows a 2.

Billy "And the champ of the world makes his move!"

Billy rolls the dice and it shows
a 5. He moves his marker.

Billy "One, two, three, four, five!
Reading Railroad. Yup, I'm gonna
buy it. Your turn."

Luis rolls the dice. It also shows
a 5. He moves his marker onto
Reading Railroad.

Billy "Aha! That's mine! Hand over
the cash, boy!"

The boys continue to play Monopoly® for over an hour. Eventually Billy wins. This time he does his victory dance on top of the kitchen table.

Luis "Stop dancing, will ya? I challenge you to another game. Got any playing cards? I'll show you!"

CHAPTER 3

Snap!

Billy gets out a pack of cards and shuffles them. He divides them into two halves and hands one half of the cards to Luis.

Billy "Okay, d'ya know how to play Snap?"

Luis "Umm, duh! Of course I do. Now *this* game I know I can beat you at!"

Billy "Yeah, keep dreaming! 'Cause remember I'm the king of..."

Luis "Yeah, yeah, the king of all games. I got it. But not this one! Let's play!"

Billy and Luis place their cards on the table, one on top of the other, watching for their chance to win.

Billy "Snap!"
Billy "Snap!"
Luis "Snap!"
Billy "Snap!"
Billy "Snap!"

Luis begins to feel frustrated as it looks like Billy is going to win again. Luis imagines that Billy is a fly and that he is about to swat him with his giant hand.

Luis "Snap!"

Billy "That's not a match! Where's your head? What are y'thinking?"

Luis "Nothin'. Just daydreaming."

Billy "Well, I wouldn't daydream if I were you. That's no way to beat a world champion like myself. Snap!"

A few minutes later the game is over. Luis has lost...again. Billy suddenly does a handstand.

Luis "Now what are you doing?"

Billy "Well, I got bored with my victory dance. So this is my victory handstand. I am the *greatest*! And you're not!"

Luis (whispering to himself) "What a show-off! I have to beat him at something. But what?...I know!"

CHAPTER 4

Noble Knight

Luis suggests that he and Billy try their hand at chess.

Billy (chuckling) "Chess?"

Luis "What? You chicken? Scared that I'm actually gonna beat you this time?"

Billy "Ha! Yeah, right! I'm the king of chess too, y'know! So, are you sure you wanna lose another game?"

Luis "There's no way I'm gonna lose this one. Chess is a thinking person's game. You need brains to play."

Billy (snorting) "Then, dude, you're gonna get whipped again!"

Billy runs up to his bedroom and returns a few moments later with a chessboard and its pieces.

Billy "Okay, I'll move my knight here."

Luis "Then I'll move my knight and take your bishop, thanks very much!"

Billy "That was dumb, 'cause now I can take your queen."

Luis starts to daydream again. He imagines that he and Billy are noble knights on their horses, about to charge at each other.

Billy "Come on! Stop daydreaming. Your move."

Luis "Aha! Gotcha! My king strikes and takes your poor old queen."

Billy "Yes!"

Luis "What? What did I do?"

CHAPTER 5

Just One More

Luis worriedly looks down at the chessboard while Billy is grinning from ear to ear.

Billy "You just blew it! Checkmate!"

Luis "What? No way! How?"

Billy "See my knight? And there it goes. Say good-bye to your king!"

Billy jumps to his feet and breaks out into his victory dance. Luis drops his head into his hands.

Billy "Hey, it's okay. You can't expect to be good at everything. You just can't beat me at games. I told you I was the king."

Luis "But even kings can lose their crowns, y'know."

Billy "Yeah, but not me. Hey, still friends?"

Luis "Guess so. But if you were a real friend you'd let me choose one more game."

Billy "Luis, you don't want to…"

Luis "Come on, just one more!"

Billy "Fine! But don't cry like a baby when I crush you again. What game do you want to play?"

Luis "What about Rock, Paper, Scissors?"

Billy "Sure!"

Luis "And if I win, then will you forget all the games you've won today and crown me the king of all games?"

Billy "Yeah, okay."

Luis "What? Really?"

Billy "Yup, really, 'cause you're just gonna lose again anyway."

Luis and Billy clench their fists and think about whether to make the action for rock, paper, or scissors.

Billy "Wait up. Paper beats rock 'cause you can cover the rock with it, right?"

Luis "Yup."

Billy "And scissors beats paper 'cause they can cut through it. And rock beats scissors 'cause it can crush the scissors. Right?"

Luis "Yup. That's it. I thought you said you were king of all games."

Billy "I am, and don't you forget it. So, bring it on. I can feel another dance coming!"

Luis and Billy shake their fists.

Billy and Luis "One, two, three!"

Luis makes the action for paper while Billy makes a rock shape.

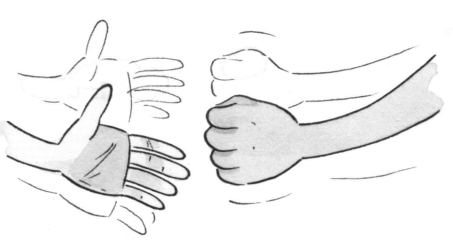

Luis "I've won! I've won! I've finally won! I'm the king of all games!"

Luis suddenly dances around Billy.

Luis "Hey, this is the coolest victory dance ever! I just wanted to save the best till last!"

Billy

BOYZ RULE!
Games Lingo

Luis

dice Small cubes with a different number of dots on each side, from 1 up to 6. If there's only one cube, it's called a die. More than one, it's dice.

friend The perfect person to play a game with!

game An activity that is entertaining and fun.

joystick A control device on a computer or video game that guides you on screen.

Monopoly® A board game where you can buy properties, houses, and hotels with fake money.

victory When you have beaten your opponent.

Games Musts

☞ Try to keep all of your board games in one spot so that you know where to find them the next time you want to play them.

☞ Be gracious when you win. No one likes a show-off.

☞ Don't go too crazy with a joystick— it could break.

☞ Find a large flat surface to play your games on, such as the kitchen table or the floor.

☞ Have plenty of snacks and drinks nearby…to help you concentrate and play better. It's tiring stuff, competing!

☞ Make up your own games. Use pencils and paper to design your own board game and decide on some rules of play.

☞ Always have fun. Remember…it's only a game!

☞ Games that don't need any equipment to play them are often the most fun, especially on long car trips. Invent some memory games and remember to remember the rules!

☞ Have your own Battle of the Games with some friends, but you have to make up your own victory dance if you win!

BOYZ RULE!

Games Instant Info

The most expensive Monopoly® set in the world is worth $2 million dollars. It's made out of gold, rubies, sapphires, and diamonds.

One of the greatest chess players in the world is Gary Kasparov from Russia.

The largest jigsaw puzzle you can buy contains 18,000 pieces, and its image is of four ancient world maps.

Five fun board games to play are Scrabble®, Monopoly®, Battleship®, Life®, and Clue®.

The most dominoes ever toppled was 3,847,295. The domino structure was built by 100 people and included a 16.5 foot (5 meter) pyramid.

Bingo is played around the world by a lot of older people.

Fish is the name of a (really easy) card game.

Chutes and Ladders®, based on an early Indian game called Moksha-Patamu, was first played in England in 1892.

There are dozens of special editions of Monopoly®, including versions based on *The Simpsons*, *The Lord of the Rings*, and NASCAR.

The tallest house of cards built was 25.29 feet (7.71 meters) tall—that's 131 storeys high!

Think Tank

1 How many different games do Luis and Billy play? What are they?

2 What game does Luis finally win?

3 What's the highest number of dots on one side of a die?

4 Is there a "prince" piece in the game of chess?

5 What are the rules to rock, paper, scissors?

6 Every time Billy wins a game he does a victory dance. How do you think this makes Luis feel?

7 What do you do when you win a game? How about when you lose?

8 What is your favorite game? Why is it your favorite?

Answers

8 Answers will vary.

7 Answers will vary.

6 Answers will vary.

5 Paper beats rock because paper covers rock; rock beats scissors because rock can crush scissors, scissors beats paper because scissors can cut paper.

4 No, there's a king and a queen but no prince.

3 The highest number of dots on one side of a die is six.

2 Luis finally wins at rock, paper, scissors.

1 Luis and Billy play five different games: a computer game; Monopoly®; a card game; chess; and rock, paper, scissors.

How did you score?

- If you got most of the answers correct, then you definitely love to play games and have the right to call yourself the king of all games!

- If you got more than half of the answers correct, you're also a great game player, but probably need to brush up on the rules sometimes.

- If you got less than half of the answers correct, then games don't seem to interest you much. But you'll always be around to join in if your friends want you to play.

Felice → ← Phil

Hi Guys!

We have lots of fun reading and want you to, too. We both believe that being a good reader is really important and so cool.

Try out our suggestions to help you have fun as you read.

At school, why don't you use "Battle of the Games" as a play and you and your friends can be the actors. Set the scene for your play. Bring some games to school to use as props but leave your computers at home! And make sure the desk you use for the victory dance is strong enough.

So...have you decided who is going to be Billy and who is going to be Luis? Now, with your friends, read and act out our story in front of the class.

We have a lot of fun when we go to schools and read our stories. After we finish, the kids all clap really loudly. When you've finished your play your classmates will do the same. Just remember to look out the window—there might be a talent scout from a television station watching you!

Reading at home is really important and a lot of fun as well.

Take our books home and get someone in your family to read them with you. Maybe they can take on a part in the story.

Remember, reading is a whole lot of fun.

So, as the frog in the local pond would say, Read-it!

And remember, Boyz Rule!

Felice

BOYZ RULE!
When We Were Kids

Phil

Phil "I used to love playing Candy Land®!"

Felice "Oh, yeah. I remember that game. I always had trouble stopping people from eating the candy."

Phil "What? You used real candy?"

Felice "Yeah. Well, how else do you play Candy Land®?"

Phil "It's a board game, silly! You're not supposed to play with real candy!"

Felice "Oh! That explains why I never won. Everybody ate my candy!"

What a Laugh!

Q What did the mini Scrabble® set say to the mini Monopoly® set?

A I'm a little *bored*.